chinese folktales

THE MAGIC MIRROR

A Chinese folktale

Illustrations: Ajit Vasaikar

XIAWUDONG WAS A KIND-HEARTED FISHERMAN. ONE DAY HE CAUGHT A VERY BIG FISH.

THAT'S A CATCH I CAN BOAST ABOUT.

BUT—

DON'T KILL ME. IF YOU RELEASE ME, I WILL SURELY HELP YOU WHEN YOU ARE IN TROUBLE.

A TALKING FISH. AND IT MAKES PROMISES TOO! IT WOULD BE WISE TO LET IT GO.

THANK YOU! WHEN YOU ARE IN TROUBLE COME BACK TO THIS VERY SPOT AND CALL OUT. I'LL RUSH TO YOUR HELP.

VERY WELL!

I SHOULD BE ON MY WAY HOME NOW!

ON THE WAY—

A PYTHON! AND IT'S CLIMBING UP THAT ROCK TO FEAST ON THOSE EAGLETS.

2

3

I HOPE I DON'T ENCOUNTER MORE TROUBLE ON THE WAY.

HELP! HELP! HELP!

WHAT COULD THAT BE?

THAT JACKAL IS A SITTING DUCK. HEH HEH!

OH, NO!

YAAAAA!

EEEK!

SORRY, BUT THAT WAS THE ONLY WAY TO SAVE THE JACKAL.

YOU SPOIL-SPORT. YOU MADE ME MISS THE SHOT! CURSE YOU!

YOU MAY CURSE ME! BUT THE JACKAL WILL SURELY BE BLESSING ME.

XIAWUDONG WAS RIGHT. I AM INDEBTED TO YOU, MY RESCUER. IF YOU EVER NEED MY HELP COME BACK HERE AND CALL OUT FOR ME.

THAT'S VERY NICE OF YOU. THANKS! I'LL BE ON MY WAY NOW.

4

XIAWUDONG WALKED ON. SOON HE CAME TO A BEAUTIFUL TOWN.

LET ME GO! LET ME GO!

WHAT'S HE DONE?

ANOTHER UNHAPPY SUITOR BEING THROWN INTO THE DUNGEON BECAUSE HE COULD NOT PASS THE PRINCESS' TEST.

TEST? WHAT TEST?

ANYONE WISHING TO MARRY THE PRINCESS HAS TO HIDE SOME PLACE WHERE SHE CAN'T FIND HIM!

EH? IT'S SO SIMPLE!

NOT AS SIMPLE AS YOU THINK, MY FRIEND. BECAUSE SHE HAS A MAGIC MIRROR.

A MAGIC MIRROR?

YES, A MAGIC MIRROR THAT SHOWS WHERE THE MAN IS HIDING!

IT'S IMPOSSIBLE TO HIDE FROM THE PRINCESS...AND HER MAGIC MIRROR.

HEY! WHERE ARE YOU GOING?

TO SEE THE PRINCESS. I NEVER COULD RESIST A CHALLENGE!

AND SOON XIAWUDONG WAS IN THE PALACE COURTYARD.

LEAD ME TO THE PRINCESS! I HAVE COME TO SEEK HER HAND!

I'M HERE.

HIDING-PLACE? I'LL TAKE YOU TO A PLACE WHERE ALL THE MAGIC MIRRORS IN THE WORLD CAN'T SEE.

THE NEXT DAY—

HE'S NOT ON LAND. HE'S NOT IN THE LAKES, RIVERS AND OCEANS EITHER. I'LL TAKE A LOOK AT THE SKY.

THERE HE IS! RIDING ON THE BACK OF AN EAGLE.

HE'S FAILED AGAIN!

YOU'VE FAILED IN YOUR SECOND ATTEMPT TOO. I'LL GIVE YOU A LAST AND FINAL CHANCE. IT'S THE DUNGEON FOR YOU IF YOU FAIL.

XIAWUDONG WENT TO SEEK THE JACKAL'S HELP—

SAVE ME FROM THE PRINCESS' MAGIC MIRROR.

YES, I WILL!

HEY WHAT ARE YOU DOING? YOU SHOULD BE LOOKING FOR A HIDING-PLACE.

I'M DIGGING A TUNNEL—A VERY LONG TUNNEL I SHOULD SAY!

AFTER MANY HOURS—

HELLO, I'M BACK! FOLLOW ME QUICKLY.

WHERE ARE YOU TAKING ME?

TO WHERE THE TUNNEL ENDS.

AH! HERE WE ARE.

BUT WHERE ARE WE?

I'LL TELL YOU... BZZ... BZZ...

HA HA! YOU ARE AS WILY AS A... A... JACKAL!

THE NEXT MORNING THE PRINCESS COULD NOT LOCATE XIAWUDONG IN HER MAGIC MIRROR.

YOU'VE SEARCHED THE LAKES, RIVERS, OCEANS, CAVES AND EVEN THE CLOUDS. WHERE COULD HE BE?

M...MY MAGIC MIRROR HAS NEVER FAILED ME. I WILL FIND HIM.

THE PRINCESS LOOKED FOR XIAWUDONG ALL DAY, BUT FINALLY HAD TO GIVE UP. THAT EVENING—

YOUR HIGHNESS. I HAVE WON, HAVEN'T I?

YES, BUT WHERE WERE YOU HIDING?

RIGHT UNDER THE DAIS YOU ARE STANDING ON. I KNEW YOU WOULDN'T THINK OF LOOKING FOR ME THERE!

BUT HOW DID YOU GET THERE?

THROUGH AN UNDER-GROUND TUNNEL, YOUR HIGHNESS!

A TUNNEL! YOU ARE INDEED VERY CLEVER! YOU WILL MAKE A GOOD KING.

AND SO XIAWUDONG AND THE PRINCESS WERE MARRIED AMID GREAT POMP AND SPLENDOUR.

VALIANT SHU LANG

Based on a story sent by:
Sunil Prabhakar

Illustrations:
Ram Waeerkar

SHU LANG WAS GIVEN MILITARY TRAINING BY HER FATHER, A CHINESE GENERAL, FROM HER EARLY CHILDHOOD. ONE DAY —

RUSSIA HAS DECLARED WAR ON CHINA. I HAVE RETIRED FROM THE ARMY. I WISH THERE WAS SOMEONE FROM OUR FAMILY TO FIGHT FOR THE COUNTRY.

FATHER, MAY I GO? I'VE LEARNT ALL THE SKILLS FROM YOU.

THE GENERAL HESITATED AT FIRST. AFTER MUCH PERSUASION—

OKAY, YOU MAY. BUT BE CAREFUL.

SHU LANG DRESSED UP AS A MAN AND SET OFF FOR THE CAPITAL. ON THE WAY —

HELLO THERE! WHERE ARE YOU GOING?

TO THE CAPITAL TO JOIN THE KING'S ARMY.

I'M GOING THERE TOO. MY NAME IS CHANG, WHAT'S YOURS?

I'M MING. LET'S TRAVEL TOGETHER.

THEY BECAME GOOD FRIENDS.

AFTER TWO DAYS, THEY REACHED THE CAPITAL AND UNDERWENT TRAINING.

A WEEK LATER, THEY WERE SENT TO THE WAR FRONT.

SHU LANG FOUGHT LIKE A RAGING TIGER. HER BRAVERY STUNNED THE RUSSIANS AS WELL AS THE CHINESE.

TAKE THIS.. AND THAT.

MING IS EXCELLENT.

THE WAR WENT ON FOR MANY DAYS. NO ONE KNEW THAT SHU LANG WAS A GIRL. NOT EVEN HER BEST FRIEND, CHANG.

AS SOON AS THE WAR IS OVER, I'LL GO IN SEARCH OF A BRIDE.

ONE DAY THE KING CALLED FOR SHU LANG.

I'VE NOTICED YOUR PROWESS ON THE BATTLEFIELD. FROM NOW ON YOU'LL LEAD THE ARMY.

THE CHINESE PUT UP A BRAVE FIGHT UNDER SHU LANG'S LEADERSHIP. ONE DAY —

SIR, WE HAVE HEARD THAT THE RUSSIANS ARE PLANNING TO ATTACK US TONIGHT.

SHU LANG HAD A PLAN FOR THAT TOO. SHE ASSEMBLED ALL THE SOLDIERS.

POSITION YOURSELVES ON THE ROOF TOPS AND WAIT FOR MY COMMAND.

THAT NIGHT —

THE CITY IS SLEEPING. VICTORY WILL BE OURS. SPREAD YOUR- SELVES THROUGH THE STREETS AND ATTACK.

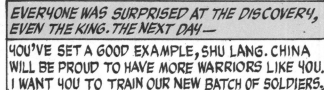

Why Cocks Eat Worms!
A Chinese Tale

Illustrator: Prachi Killekar
Colourist: Umesh Sarode

COCKS, IN ANCIENT TIMES, HAD HORNS. ONE DAY A COCK WAS WALKING AROUND IN A YARD WHEN SUDDENLY –

WHAT'S THAT SOUND?

WHOR-R-

OH, IT'S A DRAGON!

GREETINGS, HONOURABLE COCK!

GREETINGS, NOBLE DRAGON!

I'M ON MY WAY TO THE HEAVENLY REGIONS TO PAY MY RESPECTS TO THE HEAVENLY ONES.

THAT IS GOOD.

BUT...

YES....?

EVERYBODY WHO GOES TO THE HEAVENLY REGIONS MUST WEAR HORNS...AND I HAVE NONE!

I CAN SEE THAT.

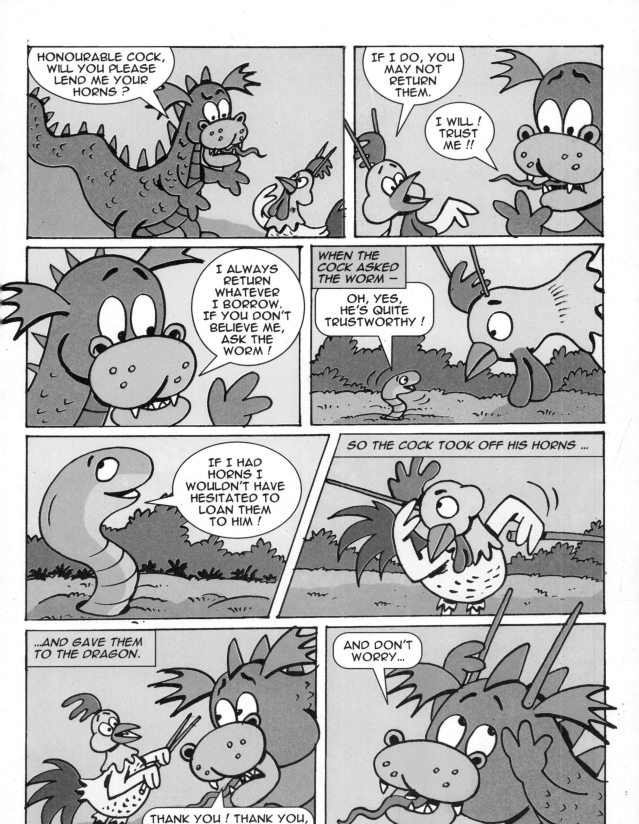

13

...I'LL RETURN THEM TO YOU ON MY WAY HOME IN THE EVENING.

BUT THE DRAGON DID NOT COME THAT EVENING. WHEN HE DID NOT SHOW UP THE NEXT DAY TOO, THE COCK BEGAN TO GET WORRIED.

HE WENT TO THE WORM.

YOUR FRIEND HASN'T COME AS YET, SIR.

HE'LL COME, HE'LL COME!

IF NOT TODAY, WELL, CERTAINLY TOMORROW!

THE COCK'S HOPES OF GETTING HIS HORNS BACK DIMINISHED WITH EACH PASSING DAY...

...AND FINALLY HE REALISED THE BITTER TRUTH —

I'VE BEEN CHEATED! I WAS A FOOL TO HAVE TRUSTED THAT DRAGON...

...AND THAT WORM!

IT'S UNLIKELY I'LL MEET THE DRAGON AGAIN....

BUT THAT WORM WON'T ESCAPE ME!

THE ANGRY COCK SEIZED THE WORM...

HEY !

...AND GULPED IT DOWN.

TO HIS SURPRISE —

IT WAS TASTY !

LET ME SEE IF I CAN FIND ANOTHER ONE !

HE WAS SO BUSY LOOKING FOR WORMS THAT HE FORGOT ALL ABOUT HIS HORNS, WHICH HE NEVER GOT BACK.

COCKS, TO THIS DAY, ARE FOND OF WORMS !

The Laughing Monks

Illustrator: Goutam Sen
Colourist: Rajesh Phatak

THREE MONKS USED TO TRAVEL ALL OVER THE COUNTRY. WHEREVER THEY WENT THEY WOULD STAND IN THE MARKETPLACE AND...

...LAUGH !!

HAHAHA !

HOOHOOHOO !

?!

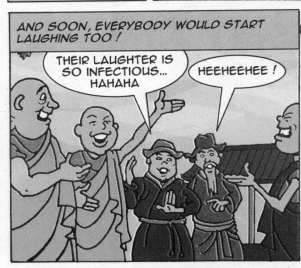

AND SOON, EVERYBODY WOULD START LAUGHING TOO !

THEIR LAUGHTER IS SO INFECTIOUS... HAHAHA

HEEHEEHEE !

IF YOU HAVE PROBLEMS...

IF YOU HAVE WORRIES...

...LAUGH AND YOU'LL FEEL BETTER !

WHAT ARE YOUR NAMES, REVERED SIRS ?

YOU CAN CALL US 'THE CLOWNS' !

HAHA...

HOHO...

LAUGHTER WAS THEIR ONLY SERMON AND THEY TRAVELLED FAR AND WIDE TO SPREAD ITS JOY.

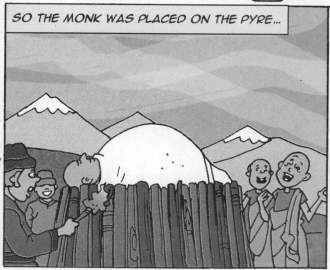

18

THE GREAT DISCOVERY

Based on a Chinese folktale
sent by : S. Sujay,

Illustrations : Ram Waeerkar

MING LIVED IN THE VILLAGE OF YUN YANG WITH HIS WIFE, LIN.

LET US HOPE FOR A GOOD HARVEST THIS TIME. WE NEED TO SAVE SOME MONEY BEFORE THE NEW YEAR.

JUST THEN —

MING, LOOK AT THAT BIRD THERE.

WHAT IS IT?

IT WAS A MAGNIFICENT BIRD.

IT IS THE PHOENIX! COME ON, MING.

BUT WHY?

IT IS A VERY LUCKY BIRD. MY MOTHER ONCE TOLD ME THAT THERE IS ALWAYS A GREAT TREASURE WHERE THE PHOENIX ALIGHTS.

LET US GO GET IT.

BY THE TIME THEY REACHED THE SPOT THE PHOENIX HAD FLOWN AWAY.

LET US BEGIN DIGGING HERE.

19

20

ARE YOU TRYING TO MAKE A FOOL OF ME? HOW DARE YOU WASTE MY TIME LIKE THIS?

BUT..M.. MY..LORD.. THE..PHOE.. PHOENIX.....

QUIET! GUARDS, TAKE THIS MAN AWAY TO THE DUNGEONS. AND THROW AWAY THAT BAG OF SAND. PRECIOUS, INDEED!

NO..NO.. PLEASE...

MING WAS THROWN INTO THE DUNGEON. A GUARD WAS CARRYING MING'S SACK OUT WHEN —

GRUNT! THIS SACK IS SO HEAVY. I'LL ASK CHANG IF I CAN LEAVE IT HERE.

CHANG WAS THE JUNIOR COOK.

CHANG AGREED —

JUST LEAVE IT UP THERE.

MANY MANY DAYS LATER —

MMMM..PERFECT MUSHROOM DUMPLINGS. I HOPE THE KING LIKES THEM TOO.

JUST THEN —

TCCCH! I MUST ASK THE GUARD TO TAKE THAT SACK OF SAND AWAY.

PLOP

CHANG, BRING THE MUSHROOMS.

UH..UH!I HAD BETTER SERVE THE MUSH- ROOMS ELSE THE KING WILL GET ANGRY.

AND — MUSHROOM DUMPLINGS, SIRE.

I HOPE HE CANNOT TELL THAT SOME SAND HAS FALLEN IN.

A LITTLE LATER — THE KING WANTS TO SEE YOU.

OH, NO. NOW I AM DONE FOR.

TELL ME, WHAT HAVE YOU PUT IN THE MUSHROOMS?

M..MY..LORD. I..UH..UM...

SPEAK UP!

QUAKING WITH FEAR CHANG CONFESSED ALL.

AND THEN TO EVERYBODY'S SURPRISE —

I LOVED THE MUSHROOM DUMPLINGS. I WANT ALL THE COOKS TO USE THE SPECIAL SAND IN WHATEVER THEY COOK.

FREE THE MAN WHO BROUGHT IT TO ME. I WILL REWARD HIM RICHLY. HE WILL ALSO SUPPLY ME WITH MORE OF THIS MAGICAL SAND.

MANY DAYS LATER —

I TOLD YOU THE PHOENIX BRINGS GREAT TREASURES.

THE TREASURE THAT MING AND LIN HAD FOUND WAS SALT.

FA-HEIN'S TREASURE

Based on a Chinese folk-tale
sent by :
Vishal Patil,

Illustrations : Atul Sriwardhan

FA-HEIN WAS OBSESSED WITH THE CONCEPT OF TURNING COPPER INTO GOLD.

THIS EXPERIMENT TOO HAS FAILED. BUT I KNOW I WILL TURN COPPER INTO GOLD SOME DAY.

HISS

CHE-MEIN, HIS WIFE, WAS VERY WORRIED.

HE HAS SQUANDERED ALMOST ALL THE ANCESTRAL WEALTH ON HIS FOOLISH DREAMS.

SHE CONSULTED A FRIEND OF HER LATE FATHER'S. THEN —

DO AS I HAVE TOLD YOU. SEND FA-HEIN TO ME TOMORROW.

I WILL. THANK YOU.

THE NEXT DAY, WHEN FA-HEIN VISITED HIM —

SINCE I HAVE NO CHILDREN, I WOULD LIKE TO PASS ON A FAMILY SECRET TO YOU.

WHAT IS IT?

IT IS AN ANCESTRAL SECRET. I KNOW HOW TO TURN COPPER INTO GOLD.

WHAT!

I SHALL TEACH YOU THIS MAGIC. BUT, FIRST, YOU MUST BRING ME THE FALLEN LEAVES OF COCONUT PALMS WATERED FROM COPPER VESSELS.

THIS MEANS I WILL HAVE TO GROW THEM MYSELF AND IT WILL TAKE A LONG TIME.

YES, IT WILL. BUT IT WILL BE WORTHWHILE.

FA-HEIN GREW A COCONUT PLANTATION ON HIS ANCESTRAL LAND. THEN—

YOU NEED THE FALLEN LEAVES, NOT THE COCONUTS... CAN I TAKE THE COCONUTS?

WELL... ALL RIGHT, YOU CAN.

WHILE FA-HEIN WAS BUSY COLLECTING THE FALLEN LEAVES...

... CHE-MEIN WAS BUSY SELLING THE COCONUTS AND THE COIR.

AFTER A FEW YEARS—

I HAVE COLLECTED ENOUGH LEAVES. CAN WE PERFORM THE MAGIC NOW?

HA! HA! THE MAGIC HAS ALREADY BEEN PERFORMED.

WHAT DO YOU MEAN? WE HAVEN'T DONE ANYTHING!

WHILE YOU WERE COLLECTING THE FALLEN LEAVES, CHE-MEIN WAS BUSY SELLING THE COCONUT AND THE COIR.

AND THIS IS ALL THE PROFIT WE HAVE MADE.

YOU MEAN ALL THIS GOLD IS OURS?

YES.

YOU HAVE TRULY PERFORMED A MIRACLE.

SO HAVE YOU AND CHE-MEIN WITH A LITTLE TOIL. HA! HA! HA!

THE FORGOTTEN VAT

Based on a Chinese folktale
sent by:
B. Surya Chakradhar

Script : Reena I. Puri

Illustrations : Chandu

IN THE CITY OF LUOYANG, IN CHINA, LIVED DUKANG. HE WAS A WONDERFUL WINE-MAKER.

A BOTTLE FOR ME DUKANG.

AND ONE FOR ME.

ONE DAY —

I HAVE BEEN MAKING WINE FOR THE LAST TWENTY-ONE YEARS, WITHOUT A BREAK. I NEED TO GO AWAY FOR A WHILE.

TAKE A HOLIDAY. YOU DESERVE IT.

THE DAY AFTER HE HAD GONE —

WINE-MAKER DUKANG, THE EMPEROR COMMANDS YOU TO HIS COURT TO MAKE WINE.

OH DEAR, BUT MY HUSBAND HAS GONE AWAY AND WILL NOT BE BACK FOR A LONG TIME.

THE EMPEROR WILL CUT OFF OUR HEADS IF WE RETURN WITHOUT DUKANG. WE WILL HAVE TO TAKE ONE OF YOUR SONS.

I HAVE ONLY ONE SON, AND HE IS A BOY OF 14. PLEASE SPARE HIM.

BUT THE GUARDS WOULD NOT LISTEN AND THE YOUNG BOY, YUMA, HAD TO GO WITH THEM.

TAKE THESE GRAPES AND THIS GRAIN WITH YOU. YOUR FATHER USED THEM TO MAKE WINE. MAY THE EMPEROR BE KIND TO YOU.

DON'T WORRY, MOTHER. I WILL BE ALL RIGHT.

THEY TRAVELLED FOR FIVE DAYS TILL THEY REACHED THE CELESTIAL CITY OF THE EMPEROR.

YUMA WAS BROUGHT BEFORE THE EMPEROR. BUT—

IMBECILES! IGNORAMUSES! THROW THESE MEN OUTSIDE THE GREAT WALL. I WANT THE MASTER WINE-MAKER, NOT A CHILD.

THE GUARDS WERE LED OFF TO THE GREAT WALL...

...AND YUMA WAS PUT OUTSIDE THE CITY WALL. DON'T EVER TRY TO ENTER THE CITY.

POOR YUMA! HE WAS ALL ALONE IN A STRANGE LAND.

HE WANDERED FROM CITY TO CITY DOING SMALL JOBS FOR PEOPLE.

AFTER A FEW MONTHS —

I AM BACK OUTSIDE THE CELESTIAL CITY BUT THIS TIME I AM NOT FRIGHTENED AND HELPLESS.

YUMA HAD EARNED ENOUGH TO RENT A TINY ROOM OUTSIDE THE CELESTIAL CITY.

I HAVE BEEN CARRYING THE GRAIN THAT MOTHER GAVE ME. I'LL PUT IT IN THIS VAT.

YUMA COVERED THE GRAIN WITH WATER AND THEN FORGOT ABOUT IT.

ALMOST TWO WEEKS LATER—

PHEW! IT'S HOT OUTSIDE. MY THROAT IS PARCHED...

... AND THERE'S NO WATER IN THE JUG.

AHA! I'LL DRINK THE WATER IN THAT VAT.

MMM.. WHAT A STRANGE AND LOVELY SMELL.

YUMA TASTED THE WATER.

IT'S DELICIOUS! I MUST CALL MY FRIENDS.

YUMA'S FRIENDS LIKED THE TASTE TOO.

IT ISN'T WINE. IT'S DIFFERENT.

I PUT A LITTLE ON THESE NOODLES. IT HAS IMPROVED THE TASTE.

YUMA'S LIQUID WAS FOUND TO EVEN CURE ILLNESSES.

THE CU-CU* YOU GAVE ME CURED MY COLD.

*CU-CU IN CHINESE MEANS VINEGAR.

27

ONE DAY— HEAR YE! HEAR YE! THE GREAT EMPEROR MING PING IS DANGEROUSLY ILL. A FISH BONE IS STUCK IN HIS THROAT AND HE IS DYING...

POOR MING PING! AFTER ALL THE HEADS HE HAS CHOPPED, HIS OWN THROAT IS IN TROUBLE.

...ANYONE WHO CAN HELP MUST COME TO THE PALACE AT ONCE. HE WILL BE RICHLY REWARDED.

I MUST TRY MY LUCK WITH THE CU-CU.

SO—

YOUR MAJESTY, SIP THIS LIQUID SLOWLY. LET IT WASH DOWN YOUR THROAT.

THE VINEGAR SOFTENED THE FISH BONE AND THE PHYSICIAN PULLED IT OUT EASILY.

AAAH! IT IS OUT!

GROAN! WHAT A RELIEF!

YOU HAVE WORKED A MIRACLE. WHO ARE YOU? WHERE IS YOUR HOME?

SIRE, ONLY THE GUARDS YOU HAVE BANISHED OVER THE GREAT WALL KNOW MY HOME.

AND YUMA REMINDED THE EMPEROR OF HIS STORY.

THE EMPEROR RECALLED THE GUARDS IMMEDIATELY. YOU WILL BRING YOUR PARENTS AND LIVE FOR AS LONG AS YOU LIKE WITH ME.

THANK YOU, SIRE.

DUKANG BECAME THE EMPEROR'S WINE-MAKER AND YUMA'S VINEGAR FOUND A VERY SPECIAL PLACE ON THE EMPEROR'S DINING TABLE.

THE LONG-HAIRED MAIDEN

Based on a Chinese folktale sent by: Salama Yamini,

Illustrations: Souren Roy

RAVEN HAIR WAS A BEAUTIFUL GIRL WHO LIVED IN A VILLAGE AT THE FOOT OF A HIGH MOUNTAIN.

SHE IS SO LOVELY. I WILL MAKE HER MY BRIDE ONE DAY.

IT WAS XIAO YONG. HE HAD LOVED RAVEN HAIR FROM THE DAYS THEY HAD PLAYED TOGETHER AS CHILDREN.

ONE DAY DISASTER BEFELL THE VILLAGE.

THE SPRING IS DRY. THERE IS NOT A DROP OF WATER IN IT.

OH NO!

WE WILL HAVE TO GO TO THE SPRING ON YONDER MOUNTAIN FOR WATER.

THAT'S THREE MILES AWAY. HOW CAN WE BRING WATER FOR OUR FIELDS?

AND SO —

LOOK, PINK-TOES, THE FIELDS ARE DRY. WE WILL HAVE TO LIVE ON ROOTS AND BARK.

GRUNT

RAVEN HAIR WOULD ROAM FAR INTO THE MOUNTAINS IN SEARCH OF FOOD. ONE DAY —

PINK-TOES, LOOK! A CLUMP OF TURNIPS.

OINK! OINK!

29

UH... HU, IT'S TOUGH TO...

... PULL! OUCH!

SPLASH

PINK-TOES, I'VE FOUND WATER! LET'S TELL EVERYONE.

SUDDENLY—

WHOOSH

THUD

OH!

AND THEN...

AAAA-EEEE!

WHOOOOSH

... A GUST OF WIND SWIRLED AROUND RAVEN HAIR AND CARRIED HER HIGH UP INTO A MOUNTAIN CAVE.

WHO ARE YOU?

I AM THE DEMON OF THIS MOUNTAIN. IF YOU TELL ANYONE ABOUT THE SPRING I WILL KILL YOU.

BEFORE SHE COULD SAY ANYTHING ANOTHER GUST OF WIND BLEW RAVEN HAIR BACK TO THE MOUNTAINSIDE.

OH, PINK-TOES, WE CANNOT TELL ANYONE OF THIS HIDDEN WATER OR I'LL DIE.

THE CROPS HAVE WITHERED, THE FIELDS ARE DRY. IF ONLY I COULD TELL EVERYONE ABOUT THE SPRING.

THE THOUGHT WORRIED RAVEN HAIR SO MUCH THAT SHE BECAME PALE AND THIN AND HER LOVELY BLACK HAIR GREW SNOW-WHITE.

SOMETHING IS WORRYING RAVEN HAIR. BUT SHE WILL NOT SPEAK A WORD.

ONE DAY XIAO YONG'S FATHER WAS BRINGING HOME A BUCKET OF WATER WHEN—

AAAH!

UNCLE YONG!

THE WATER! IT'S FLOWING AWAY. STOP IT!

UNCLE YONG, YOU'RE HURT. DON'T TRY TO GET UP. THE WATER HAS GONE INTO THE GROUND.

THAT NIGHT— POOR UNCLE YONG, HE WAS SO BADLY HURT YET HE COULD ONLY THINK ABOUT THE WATER. I CANNOT KEEP QUIET ANY LONGER.

32

THE FIENDS AND THE MOUNTAIN DEMON WHISKED RAVEN HAIR OUT OF THE CAVE.

OH! IT'S A GIANT WATERFALL

COME ALONG, MY PRETTY.

THE FIENDS BOUND HER TO A ROCK IN THE WATERFALL.

SHE HAS FAINTED.

THE DELICATE LITTLE THING. SERVES HER RIGHT.

SHE CAN STAY THERE FOREVER.

MEANWHILE —

WHERE IS RAVEN HAIR?

SHE IS NOT IN THE VILLAGE.

WHERE COULD SHE BE?

XIAO YONG WAS FRANTIC WITH WORRY AND SEARCHED HIGH AND LOW FOR RAVEN HAIR. FINALLY—

OH, BANYAN TREE, IF ONLY YOU COULD SPEAK YOU'D TELL ME WHERE I CAN FIND MY RAVEN HAIR.

I CAN TELL YOU, XIAO YONG.

WHAT! YOU CAN SPEAK? PLEASE TELL ME.

SHE HAS BEEN TAKEN BY THE MOUNTAIN DEMON, WHO LIVES FAR AWAY FROM HERE NEAR STRONG WATER...

... HE HAS TURNED HER INTO A STONE. HE WILL TURN YOU ALSO INTO A STONE, IF YOU GO THERE.

IS THERE NOTHING I CAN DO? I WOULD RISK MY LIFE TO SAVE MY RAVEN HAIR.

FIRST GO TO THE OYSTER FAIRY WHO LIVES IN THE GANDOMA SEA ...

... ASK HER TO GIVE YOU HER FLUTE. NO HARM CAN COME TO YOU AS LONG AS YOU PLAY THE FLUTE.

XIAO YONG TRAVELLED OVER NINETY-NINE MOUNTAINS TO REACH THE GANDOMA SEA. THERE —

YOU CALLED ME, YOUNG MAN?

YES, OYSTER FAIRY. I NEED YOUR HELP AND HAVE TRAVELLED FAR FOR IT.

AFTER SHE HAD HEARD THE STORY, THE OYSTER FAIRY GAVE XIAO YONG A GOLDEN FLUTE.

KEEP PLAYING ON IT AND YOU WILL BE SAFE.

I WILL DO AS YOU TELL ME, GOOD FAIRY.

AND SO —

A GOLDEN LIGHT EMANATES FROM THE FLUTE WHEN I PLAY IT. AH, I FEEL SO SAFE!

WHEN THE FIENDS AND THE MOUNTAIN DEMON SAW XIAO YONG APPROACHING —

HE HAS GOT THE ARMOUR OF MAGIC LIGHT.

QUICK! TAKE THE MAIDEN AND LET US BE OFF.

STOP! DON'T TAKE RAVEN HAIR AWAY.

STOP US IF YOU CAN.

34

I MUSTN'T STOP PLAYING OR THEY'LL KILL ME.

HA! HA! HEE! HEE! HOO! HOO!

THE FIENDS CARRIED RAVEN HAIR HIGH UP ON A MOUNTAIN AND —

NO-O-O! DON'T THROW HER.

THAT WE WILL. AND YOU CAN WATCH HER BREAK INTO A THOUSAND PIECES.

AS THE FIENDS THREW RAVEN HAIR —

YOU CAN'T DO THIS. AAAH!

AS THE TWO FELL DOWN THE CLIFF, XIAO YONG KEPT PLAYING THE FLUTE AND AS THE MUSIC FLOWED FROM IT—

THE GOLDEN LIGHT IS CARRYING US DOWN. SAFELY.

OH... HUH!

RAVEN HAIR, YOU ARE NO LONGER A STONE STATUE.

XIAO YONG, YOU'VE SAVED ME! I THOUGHT I'D NEVER SEE YOU AGAIN.

THE VILLAGERS WERE DELIGHTED TO SEE RAVEN HAIR AND XIAO YONG COME BACK...

...AND CELEBRATED THEIR GOOD FORTUNE WITH JOY. AS FOR THE MOUNTAIN DEMON HE WAS HELPLESS BECAUSE THE MAGIC FLUTE GUARDED THE COUPLE TILL THE END OF THEIR LIVES.

CHEATING THE CHEAT
A CHINESE FOLKTALE

Based on a story sent by:
James Tongoe

Illustrations:
Archana Amberkar

IN ORDER TO EARN SOME EXTRA MONEY, CHU YANG HAD SENT HIS TWO OLDER SONS TO WORK FOR FU YON, A RICH MAN IN THE NEIGHBOURING VILLAGE. BUT BOTH WERE NOW BACK, EMPTY-HANDED.

HE'S A CHEAT, PA. HE MAKES US WORK HARD AND THEN FINDS A WAY NOT TO PAY US.

BUT HOW...?

HE TRIES SO MANY TRICKS! HE'S TOO CLEVER.

NOT AS CLEVER AS ME. I'D LIKE TO GO AND TRY MY LUCK, PA.

YOU! BUT YOU'RE ONLY FOURTEEN!

IT WAS HU TAN, CHU YANG'S YOUNGEST SON.

EVENTUALLY, HU TAN'S WISH PREVAILED AND HE WENT TO FU YON'S HOUSE.

ALL RIGHT, I'LL HIRE YOU. BUT YOU MUST OBEY EVERY WORD OF MINE. IF YOU DON'T YOU WON'T GET PAID AT ALL.

HMM... SMART MAN.

AS YOU SAY, MASTER.

HU TAN WORKED HARD AND SINCERELY FOR A FEW DAYS. THEN —

HU TAN, I WANT YOU TO TAKE MY BULLOCK TO FEED ON BAMBOO LEAVES.

YES, MASTER.

BUT DON'T USE YOUR HANDS TO PULL DOWN THE LEAVES FROM THE TREES. AND MAKE SURE MY BULLOCK EATS.

HERE COMES TRICK NUMBER ONE. I'LL HAVE TO FIND A WAY OUT OF THIS.

36

HU TAN'S WHIPPING THE BULLOCK!

SOMEONE FETCH THE MASTER, QUICK.

HU TAN TOOK THE BULLOCK UP TO THE BAMBOO GROVE AND THEN —

EAT, EAT. YOU DUMB OAF.

WHIP

SLASH

MOOO

FU YON CAME RUNNING UP AND WAS HORRIFIED.

HU TAN! STOP! WHAT ARE YOU DOING!?

TRYING TO MAKE THE BULLOCK CLIMB UP AND EAT THE LEAVES, MASTER— SINCE I CAN'T BRING THE LEAVES DOWN.

OH! DOESN'T MATTER. STOP BEATING HIM.

THEN CAN I USE MY HANDS TO PLUCK THE LEAVES, MASTER?

YES, YES, YOU CAN. GRR....

I'M GOING TO GET YOU.

HEH HEH! GOT YOU THIS TIME. WONDER WHEN YOU'LL TRY THE NEXT TRICK.

HU TAN DIDN'T HAVE TO WAIT LONG. TWO DAYS LATER —

HU TAN! HERE ARE SOME VEGETABLES. I WANT YOU TO PLANT THEM ON THE ROOF.

YES, MASTER.

37

THUMP! THUMP! CRACK

HUH!?

EEEKS! HU TAN! WHAT ARE YOU DOING?

CRASH

I WAS DIGGING THE ROOF, MASTER, IN ORDER TO PLANT THE VEGETABLES YOU GAVE ME.

OH NO! I BROUGHT THIS UPON MYSELF!

BUT FU YON STILL WOULD NOT GIVE UP. HE DECIDED TO HAVE ONE LAST TRY.

HU TAN, I'M WORRIED THAT THE HEAT IS GOING TO KILL MY CROPS. I WANT YOU TO SHIFT MY FIELDS INTO THE HOUSE.

THIS ONE IS WILD!

THUMP BANG

THE HOUSE IS SHAKING!

WHAT'S HAPPENING?

CRASH

MY DOOR!

HU TAN HAD BROKEN DOWN THE DOOR WITH A HUGE IRON BALL.

HU TAN! YOU'VE GONE CRAZY. STOP THIS AT ONCE.

BUT I'M ONLY FOLLOWING YOUR ORDERS, MASTER.

DID I ORDER YOU TO BREAK MY HOUSE, YOU LIAR!?

NO, MASTER, YOU ORDERED ME TO MOVE THE FIELDS INTO YOUR HOUSE...

...I TRIED BUT I FOUND THE DOOR WAS TOO SMALL FOR THEM TO ENTER. SO I BROKE IT DOWN.

OH, HELP! YOU'RE EITHER EXTREMELY STUPID OR THE SMARTEST MAN I EVER SAW...

...EITHER WAY, I NEVER WANT TO SEE YOU AGAIN. PLEASE LEAVE ME IN PEACE.

BUT MY WAGES, MASTER.

HERE! HERE! TAKE YOUR WAGES AND MORE! BUT JUST GO.

THANK YOU, MASTER.

HU TAN RETURNED HOME A TRIUMPHANT BOY.

AND FU YON NEVER TRIED TO CHEAT ANYONE AGAIN.

LING DANG AND THE RED FRUIT TREE

Based on a Chinese Folk-Tale
sent by :
H.F. Caroline Liu

Illustrations:
Chandu

LING DANG LIVED WITH HIS STEPMOTHER AND HIS LITTLE STEPBROTHER BAODAN.

HURRY UP AND BRING THE HAY IN, LING DANG.

YES, MOTHER.

OH!

YOU CLUMSY BOY, YOU'VE WET ALL THE HAY. YOU CAN GO TO BED WITHOUT SUPPER.

LING DANG'S STEPMOTHER DID NOT LOVE HIM VERY MUCH...

... BUT LITTLE BAODAN DID.

PSSST, LING DANG. I HAVE BROUGHT A PIECE OF BREAD FOR YOU.

THANK YOU, BAODAN. BUT IF MOTHER COMES TO KNOW....

BUT THE LITTLE BOY DID NOT CARE AND WOULD HELP LING DANG WHENEVER HE COULD.

ONE DAY —

MAMA, WHAT SHOULD I DO TODAY?

TAKE THE SHEEP TO GRAZE IN WILD-WOLF GULLY.

I'D LIKE TO GO TOO.

NO, YOU CAN GO LATER.

THE STEPMOTHER KNEW THAT WILD-WOLF GULLY WAS A DANGEROUS PLACE.

IF THE WOLVES GET HIM THERE'LL BE ONE MOUTH LESS FOR ME TO FEED.

LING DANG SET OFF WITH THE SHEEP, BUT ON HIS WAY HE STOPPED AT THE COTTAGE OF AN OLD SHEPHERD.

GRANDFATHER, DO YOU KNOW WHERE WILD-WOLF GULLY IS?

I SURE DO. THERE'S GOOD GREEN GRASS AND SWEET SPRING WATER...

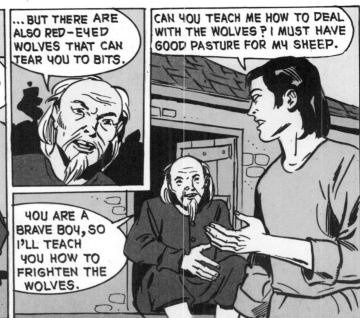

...BUT THERE ARE ALSO RED-EYED WOLVES THAT CAN TEAR YOU TO BITS.

CAN YOU TEACH ME HOW TO DEAL WITH THE WOLVES? I MUST HAVE GOOD PASTURE FOR MY SHEEP.

YOU ARE A BRAVE BOY, SO I'LL TEACH YOU HOW TO FRIGHTEN THE WOLVES.

THE OLD MAN CUPPED HIS HANDS AND BLEW HARD THROUGH THEM.

R·O·A·R

OOOH! THAT SOUNDS LIKE A TIGER! EVEN THE COTTAGE IS TREMBLING WITH FEAR.

LING DANG WAS A CLEVER BOY AND SOON MASTERED THE SOUND.

THANK YOU, GRANDFATHER I'LL BE ON MY WAY NOW.

MAY THE SPIRITS OF THE MOUNTAINS GUIDE YOUR WAY, MY SON.

WILD-WOLF GULLY WAS REALLY A BEAUTIFUL PLACE.

SUCH GREEN GRASS AND NO HERDSMEN IN SIGHT. WHAT A PITY!

LING DANG CUPPED HIS HANDS AND —

R·O·A·R

BAAA!

THAT WAS TO FRIGHTEN THE WOLVES, SILLY. NOW GO AND GRAZE AS MUCH AS YOU LIKE.

AS LING DANG CLIMBED UP A SLOPE HE SAW A FRUIT TREE.

LOOKS GOOD.

MMMM... TASTES GOOD TOO!

LET ME HAVE ANOTHER ONE TO QUENCH MY THIRST.

AS SOON AS LING DANG HAD FINISHED IT—

IT FEELS AS IF I HAVE HAD A LONG COOL DRINK. MY MIND FEELS SO FRESH...

...BUT I AM STILL HUNGRY. SO I'LL EAT ANOTHER ONE TO SATISFY MY HUNGER.

AND AS SOON AS HE ATE ANOTHER RED FRUIT—

I FEEL SO FULL. THIS IS SURELY A MAGICAL FRUIT THAT GRANTS WISHES. IT UNDERSTANDS WHAT I SAY. LET ME TRY AGAIN.

RED FRUIT, I WANT TO GROW HEALTHY AND STRONG, WITH MIGHTY MUSCLES AND A RUDDY COMPLEXION.

AFTER HE HAD EATEN THE FRUIT—

OOOH! I AM FEELING HOT AND ITCHY. I MUST HAVE A DIP IN THE STREAM.

LING DANG SPLASHED INTO THE COOL WATER...

SPLASH

... AND WHEN HE EMERGED—

LOOK AT ME! I AM AS STRONG AS AN OX, AND AS RED AS AN APPLE!

THAT EVENING AS THE SUN WAS SETTING—

WHO IS THAT COMING WITH THE SHEEP? IT IS A STRANGER. LING DANG MUST HAVE BEEN EATEN BY THE WOLVES. GOOD!

43

BUT TO HER DISMAY —

MAMA, LOOK AT ME!

LING DANG!

THAT NIGHT LING DANG TOLD THE STORY OF THE RED FRUIT TREE.

SO THAT'S HOW YOU BECAME STRONG!

YES, ISN'T IT WONDERFUL?

THE STEPMOTHER DID NOT THINK IT WAS WONDERFUL AT ALL...

... SO, THE NEXT DAY —

LING DANG, I WANT YOU TO FETCH FIREWOOD FROM THE WESTERN HILL.

YES, MAMA.

AFTER HE HAD LEFT —

BAODAN, GO TO THE WILD-WOLF GULLY AND PICK ALL THE FRUIT ON THAT TREE. WE WILL EAT THEM EVERY DAY AND MAKE A WISH.

THAT WILL BE FUN.

BAODAN SET OFF JOYFULLY.

THE DAY PASSED AND AS THE SUN SET, BAODAN'S MOTHER WAITED.

MAMA, WHO ARE YOU WAITING FOR?

FOR YOUR BROTHER! TO RETURN FROM THE WILD-WOLF GULLY.

OH NO! MAMA IT WAS WRONG OF YOU TO HAVE SENT HIM.

LING DANG, WAIT!

I AM GOING TO LOOK FOR MY BROTHER.

I AM COMING WITH YOU.

A SUDDEN STORM BLEW ACROSS THE MOUNTAINS.

BOOM

CRASH!

IT IS SO DARK. I CAN HARDLY FIND MY WAY.

WHERE COULD BAODAN BE?

AND THEN—

WOOO-OOO-OOO-OOO-OOO

GRROWR

THE WOLVES! THEY ARE AFTER BAODAN.

LING DANG FOLLOWED THE SOUND OF THE WOLVES.

THERE THEY ARE UNDER THE FRUIT TREE. NOW I UNDERSTAND! MOTHER MUST HAVE SENT BAODAN TO GET THE FRUIT.

DO SOMETHING, LING DANG. THE WOLVES ARE TEARING DOWN THE TREE.

DON'T WORRY, MOTHER.

LING DANG CUPPED THE PALMS OF HIS HANDS AND SOON—

RROAR

!?

THE WOLVES FLED IN FEAR.

BAODAN, ARE YOU THERE?

YIP! YIP! YIP! YOW! OW! OW!

THERE WAS NO ANSWER SO LING DANG CLIMBED UP THE TREE.

POOR LITTLE FELLOW, HE HAS FAINTED WITH FRIGHT. I'LL CARRY HIM HOME.

AFTER REACHING HOME BAODAN TOLD THEM HIS STORY. ... AND I HAD JUST PLUCKED TWO OF THESE FRUITS WHEN THE WOLVES ATTACKED ME.

EAT ONE, MOTHER. IT WILL DO YOU GOOD.

YOU HAVE BEEN GOOD, LING DANG. I WISH I HAD TREATED YOU BETTER.

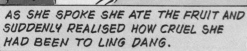

AS SHE SPOKE SHE ATE THE FRUIT AND SUDDENLY REALISED HOW CRUEL SHE HAD BEEN TO LING DANG.

MY DEAREST SON, HOW I HAVE WRONGED YOU!

I WISH WE ALWAYS REMAIN A HAPPY FAMILY.

AND THAT WAS BAODAN'S WISH WHICH, OF COURSE, CAME TRUE.

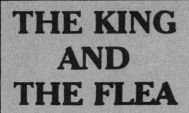

THE KING AND THE FLEA

Based on story sent by:
James Tungoe.

Ilustrations:
Savio Mascarenhas

THE PEOPLE OF CHOO KIAU WERE UNHAPPY WITH THEIR KING.

WE WILL NEVER PROSPER UNDER OUR FOOLISH KING.

YOU'RE RIGHT. I'M FED UP WITH HIS HARE-BRAINED SCHEMES.

MENU

I WISH WE COULD BANISH HIM.

SO DO I. BUT BESIDES BEING FOOLISH, HE IS RICH AND POWERFUL TOO.

NEXT DAY—

HAVE YOU HEARD THE LATEST? A DOG SNARLED AT THE KING YESTERDAY AND NOW HE WANTS ALL DOGS BANISHED FROM THE KINGDOM.

GASP! MY POOR PEE KEE.

THEIR CONVERSATION WAS OVERHEARD BY A LITTLE FLEA THAT LIVED ON PEE KEE.

WHAT! BANISH YOU! BUT YOU'RE MY HOME, PEE KEE.

AWOO! I DON'T WANT TO BE BANISHED.

DON'T HOWL, PEE KEE. I'LL ... I'LL BANISH THE KING INSTEAD.

YOU!?

YES. JUST WATCH.

AND THE LITTLE FLEA HOPPED OFF TO THE KING'S PALACE.

THAT NIGHT, AS HE SLEPT, THE FLEA BIT THE KING.

OW! WHO DARES TO DISTURB THE ROYAL SLUMBER!?

THE KING SPOTTED THE FLEA.

A FLEA! I'LL GET YOU, YOU ABOMINABLE INSECT!

BUT THE FLEA HOPPED AWAY AND HID ITSELF.

THE KING SHOOK OUT THE ROYAL BED-CLOTHES.

THERE! THAT'S GOT RID OF IT.

TEE HEE! THAT'S WHAT YOU THINK.

THE FLEA HAD HIDDEN ITSELF IN THE ROYAL BEARD.

THE KING LAY DOWN AND AGAIN, THE FLEA BIT HIM.

YOW! IT'S THE FLEA AGAIN. GUARDS! FIND THAT PESKY FLEA AT ONCE.

THE GUARDS RUSHED IN AND THE KING'S BED-CHAMBER WAS TURNED UPSIDE DOWN. FINALLY—

CHIEF PALACE GUARD REPORTING, SIRE. ALL FLEAS EXTERMINATED.

CHUCKLE! ALL EXCEPT ONE.

AND NIGHT AFTER NIGHT THE FLEA BIT THE KING, TILL AT LAST—

GROAN! MY BODY IS BLACK AND BLUE WITH FLEA BITES. I HAVEN'T SLEPT FOR DAYS... I THINK I'LL TAKE A HOLIDAY FROM BEING KING AND CATCH UP ON MY SLEEP.

SO, EARLY NEXT MORNING—

TIME TO WAKE UP, YOUR MAJESTY.

LET ME SLEEP! YOU BE THE RULER TODAY.

FOR TWO WHOLE DAYS AND NIGHTS THE KING SLEPT. AND SO DID THE FLEA.

SNORE

Z-Z-Z-Z

WHEN HE AWOKE—

I'VE NEVER FELT BETTER BEFORE. THE FLEA DID NOT BITE ME. MAYBE ...

THE FOOLISH KING THOUGHT HARD THEN—

... MAYBE IT DOES NOT BITE KINGS WHO ARE ON HOLIDAY. I ... I SHALL TAKE A HOLIDAY FOR-EVER!

THE KING SUMMONED HIS COURT AT ONCE.

MY PEOPLE, I HAVE DECIDED TO RETIRE.

WISEST DECISION HE HAS MADE.

HURRAH!

WHEN THE KING LEFT, THE FLEA HOPPED BACK ON PEE KEE.

YOU DID IT! BUT WHY DIDN'T YOU STAY ON IN THE PALACE? LIFE MUST HAVE BEEN COMFORTABLE OVER THERE.

IT WAS, PEE KEE, IT WAS. BUT THERE'S NO PLACE LIKE HOME.

AND THE FLEA SNUGGLED BACK IN PEE KEE'S FUR.

49

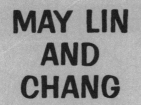

MAY LIN AND CHANG

A Chinese Folktale

Name and address
of the child not sent.

Script : Priya Khanna

Illustrations : Chandu

IN A SMALL VILLAGE IN CHINA LIVED A LOVELY GIRL CALLED MAY LIN.

MOTHER, SEE WHAT I EMBROIDERED.

AH! SUCH PRETTY NAPKINS!

MAY LIN WAS EXTREMELY GOOD AT EMBROIDERY.

SHE WAS EVERYONE'S FAVOURITE.

MAY LIN IS AS GOOD-NATURED AS SHE IS BEAUTIFUL.

MAY LIN WAS ENGAGED TO BE MARRIED TO A POOR FARMER, CHANG.

MY DEAR, I HOPE I CAN GIVE YOU A COMFORTABLE LIFE.

CHANG WAS VERY AMBITIOUS AND DREAMT OF BEING RICH ONE DAY.

THE KINGDOM WAS RULED BY QUEEN JUNG. ONE DAY AS SHE WAS TRAVELLING PAST MAY LIN'S VILLAGE —

I'M VERY THIRSTY. GET ME SOME WATER FROM THAT COTTAGE THERE.

YES, YOUR MAJESTY.

IT WAS MAY LIN'S HOUSE.

I'LL BRING SOME SNACKS TOO.

50

MAY LIN SET A TRAY WITH SOME FOOD AND NAPKINS ON IT AND TOOK IT TO THE QUEEN.

WHO MADE THESE BEAUTIFUL NAPKINS?

I DID, YOUR MAJESTY.

THE QUEEN WAS VERY IMPRESSED.

YOU DESERVE MUCH MORE THAN THIS POOR COTTAGE. I WANT YOU TO MARRY MY SON AND BE THE PRINCESS.

I'M SORRY, YOUR MAJESTY, I AM ALREADY ENGAGED TO BE MARRIED.

IMPOLITE GIRL! HOW DARE YOU REFUSE MY OFFER!

AND THE QUEEN DROVE AWAY IN GREAT ANGER.

I'LL NEVER LET THIS PROUD GIRL BE HAPPY.

CHANG AND MAY LIN SOON GOT MARRIED.

I WANT TO OWN THE LAND THAT I TILL.

WHY DON'T YOU SPEAK TO THE LANDLORD?

CHANG WORKED AS A TENANT FARMER.

THE NEXT DAY—

THE LAND IS GOING TO BE OURS FOR FIVE GOLD PIECES.

FIVE GOLD PIECES! WHERE ARE WE GOING TO ARRANGE SO MUCH MONEY FROM?

I'LL WORK HARD IN THE FIELD. YOU CAN EMBROIDER NAPKINS AND TABLECLOTH AND SELL THEM TO RICH FOLK FROM THE TOWN.

ONE DAY —

I SOLD SOME GRAIN TODAY. HERE ARE YOUR THREADS AND CLOTH.

NOW I CAN START WORKING.

SOON —

THESE ARE SO BEAUTIFUL. DO NOT SELL THESE FOR LESS THAN 20 PIECES OF SILVER.

YES, AND I'LL GO ONLY TO THAT PART OF THE TOWN WHERE RICH PEOPLE LIVE.

SHE SET OUT WITH HER LOVELY WARES BUT FOUND NO BUYER.

20 PIECES OF SILVER FOR A PIECE OF CLOTH! IT'S FAR TOO EXPENSIVE.

IT IS HAND-MADE, MADAM.

BUT IT WAS THE SAME STORY AT EVERY DOOR.

MAY LIN WAS WANDERING CLOSE TO THE PALACE WHEN —

IT'S THE PROUD GIRL WHO'D REFUSED TO MARRY MY SON. NOW I'LL TEACH HER A LESSON.

MAY LIN WAS CAUGHT BY THE GUARDS AND BROUGHT TO QUEEN JUNG.

YOU'VE COME HERE TO STEAL, HAVEN'T YOU?

CERTAINLY NOT, YOUR MAJESTY. I CAME HERE TO SELL MY WARES.

YOU REFUSED TO BE THE PRINCESS ONE DAY. NOW YOU'LL STAY HERE ALL YOUR LIFE AND EMBROIDER FOR ME.

HAVE MERCY, YOUR MAJESTY.

BUT THE CRUEL QUEEN PAID NO HEED TO MAY LIN'S CRIES.

I'LL MOVE ABOUT THE PALACE AT NIGHT AND MAKE MYSELF FAMILIAR WITH ALL THE DOORS AND PASSAGES. I MIGHT BE ABLE TO ESCAPE, THEN.

SOON MAY LIN KNEW THE BUILDING REALLY WELL.

I'LL EMBROIDER THE MAP OF THE PALACE ON THIS CLOTH. IT'LL HELP ME ESCAPE.

MEANWHILE, CHANG DISCOVERED THAT MAY LIN HAD BEEN CAPTURED BY QUEEN JUNG.

CHANG, DID YOU HEAR THAT THE CRUEL QUEEN HAS IMPRISONED A POOR VILLAGE WOMAN?

UH..NO. IT HAS TO BE MAY LIN. SHE'S NOT COME HOME FOR TWO DAYS NOW.

CHANG THOUGHT OF A PLAN TO RESCUE HIS WIFE.

HERE I GO TO GET MY MAY LIN WITH LACES, RIBBONS AND TRINKETS.

OUTSIDE THE PALACE —

WITH MY RIBBONS 'N' TRINKETS 'N' LACE, YOU'LL HAVE A SMILE ON YOUR FACE....

I WONDER WHERE SHE IS.

INSIDE THE PALACE, MAY LIN RECOGNIZED CHANG'S VOICE.

THAT SOUNDS LIKE CHANG!

IT IS CHANG!

AH! THERE SHE IS!

CHANG THREW A BALL OF PAPER TO HER...

... AND WENT AWAY BEFORE THE GUARDS COULD SEE HIM.

'MEET ME OUTSIDE THE SOUTHERN GATE OF THE TOWN AT MIDNIGHT. I'LL WAIT THERE WITH TWO HORSES.'

UMM.. SOUTHERN GATE.. THE WINDOW IN THE STORE-ROOM LOOKS OUT TOWARDS THE SOUTH....

SHE DECIDED TO TAKE THE EMBROIDERED MAP WITH HER.

THAT NIGHT SHE SNEAKED INTO THE STOREROOM...

... CLIMBED OUT OF THE WINDOW...

SO FAR, SO GOOD.

... AND RAN THROUGH THE DARK, EMPTY STREET TOWARDS THE SOUTHERN GATE.

HUFF PUFF.. I'M ALMOST THERE.

CHANG WAS WAITING THERE WITH TWO HORSES.

LET'S RIDE TO THE NEIGHBOURING KINGDOM.

THE QUEEN WILL NEVER BE ABLE TO FIND US THERE.

THEY REACHED THE NEIGHBOURING KINGDOM THE NEXT DAY.

WHY IS THIS CROWD GATHERED HERE?

WE ARE ALL HERE TO FIND A SOLUTION TO THE DISASTER THAT'S FALLEN UPON US.

OUR KING HAS DIED WITHOUT AN HEIR AND WE'VE HEARD THAT QUEEN JUNG IS GOING TO ATTACK US.

FROM THE FRYING PAN INTO THE FIRE! IT SEEMS THAT PROBLEMS CHASE US.

WELL, NOT REALLY. YOU CAN LEAD THE PEOPLE TO VICTORY WITH THIS MAP OF QUEEN JUNG'S PALACE.

YOU HAVE A MAP! HOW CLEVER YOU ARE, MAY LIN!

WITH THE HELP OF THE MAP, CHANG SEALED QUEEN JUNG'S PALACE FROM ALL SIDES.

WAKE UP, YOUR MAJESTY. YOU ARE A PRISONER NOW.

HUH?!

CHANG AND MAY LIN RULED BOTH THE KINGDOMS WELL...

... AND QUEEN JUNG SPENT HER DAYS EMBROIDERING NAPKINS.

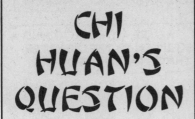

CHI HUAN'S QUESTION

Based on a story sent by :
Rashida Siddique,

Illustrations : Ram Waeerkar

LONG LONG AGO, IN A SMALL KINGDOM IN CHINA, IT WAS BELIEVED THAT ANYONE WITH THE NAME, CHI HUAN, GREW VERY RICH. ONE DAY—

THERE'S AN ORPHAN INFANT LYING BY THE VILLAGE POND. WHAT DO WE NAME HIM?

LET HIM BE KNOWN AS CHI HUAN. HE'LL GROW UP TO BE A RICH MAN.

HOWEVER, CHI HUAN GREW UP TO BE A POOR MAN.

WHY THIS INJUSTICE? WHY AM I POOR EVEN WITH THE NAME, CHI HUAN?

GO TO KUBAYA SHI AND ASK HER THIS QUESTION. LET'S SEE WHAT SHE HAS TO SAY.

WHO IS KUBAYA SHI?

SHE IS A FAIRY WHO LIVES BEYOND THE LAKE OUTSIDE OUR KINGDOM IT IS SAID THAT SHE HAS ANSWERS TO THE FIRST THREE QUESTIONS PUT TO HER.

CHI HUAN LEFT FOR KUBAYA SHI'S ABODE. SOON HE CAME TO AN INN.

WHERE ARE YOU GOING, YOUNG MAN?

I'M GOING TO KUBAYA SHI.

PLEASE DO ME A FAVOUR. ASK HER WHEN I'LL BE ABLE TO SEE THE WORLD. SOB! I WAS BORN BLIND AND I DON'T HAVE A FAMILY TO LOOK AFTER ME AND MY INN WHEN I'M OLD AND WEAK.

DON'T WORRY. I'LL COME BACK WITH THE ANSWER.

CHI HUAN RESUMED HIS JOURNEY. SOON —

WHHOOOOSH!!

STOP! WHERE ARE YOU GOING?

UH.. ER.. I'M ON MY WAY TO SEE KUBAYA SHI....

AND CHI HUAN TOLD THE DRAGON HIS STORY.

AH! MY SEARCH HAS FINALLY ENDED.

WHAT SEARCH?

I AM TWO THOUSAND YEARS OLD. I'VE BEEN LOOKING FOR A PERSON WHO'S GOING TO KUBAYA SHI FOR THE PAST FIFTEEN HUNDRED YEARS. FINALLY I HAVE FOUND YOU!

YOU'RE EXTREMELY FOOLISH.

PRAY, WHY?

WHY DIDN'T YOU GO TO KUBAYA SHI ON YOUR OWN IF YOU HAD A QUESTION? SILLY OF YOU TO HAVE WAITED FOR SO MANY YEARS.

WELL, I WAS ALL SET TO GO TO HER WHEN I WAS TOLD THAT SHE IS TERRIFIED OF DRAGONS. SO I HAD TO WAIT HERE. ANYWAY, PLEASE ASK HER WHAT I NEED TO DO TO BE THE PRESIDENT OF THE DRAGONS' CLUB.

DON'T WORRY, FRIEND. I'LL ASK HER.

A LITTLE LATER, CHI HUAN CAME TO A FIELD.

BOO HOO HOO! SOB!

WHY ARE YOU CRYING?

I HAD..SOB..WORKED VERY HARD ALL THIS SEASON AND HAD HARVESTED A VERY GOOD CROP. BUT..SOB..SOMEONE STOLE MY HARVESTED GRAIN. WHAT DO I DO NOW?

DON'T BE SAD. I'M GOING TO KUBAYA SHI. I'LL ASK HER WHAT YOU MUST DO.

THE NEXT MORNING CHI HUAN REACHED KUBAYA SHI'S PALACE.

KUBAYA SHI, I'M BURSTING WITH QUESTIONS! I'VE TO ASK YOU ABOUT THE BLIND INNKEEPER, THE OLD DRAGON, THE SAD FARMER AND MYSELF.

CHI HUAN, YOU MAY ASK ME ONLY THE FIRST THREE QUESTIONS.

POOR CHI HUAN! HE HAD TO FORGET HIS OWN QUESTIONS BUT HE GOT THE OTHER THREE ANSWERS.

I'VE GOT YOUR ANSWER! WIPE AWAY THOSE TEARS.

WHAT DID THE FAIRY SAY?

CHI HUAN ASKED THE FARMER TO LEAD HIM TO THE OLDEST TREE ON HIS FARM. THEN —

SCRAPE GLUNK!

WHAT ARE YOU DOING?

AH! JUST AS KUBAYA SHI HAD SAID! SEE, TWO POTS FULL OF GOLD COINS WERE BURIED UNDER THIS TREE BY YOUR ANCESTORS.

BLESS YOU, CHI HUAN. YOU MAY TAKE ONE POT OF GOLD.

CHI HUAN WALKED ALONG HAPPILY TO THE DRAGON.

OPEN YOUR MOUTH WITHOUT LETTING OUT ANY FLAMES.

THAT'S DIFFICULT BUT I'LL TRY.

ONE, TWO, THREE, FOUR AND FIVE! JUST AS KUBAYA SHI HAD SAID!

ULP! JUST FIVE TEETH LEFT IN MY MOUTH!

NO, YOU HAVE FIVE PEARLS IN YOUR MOUTH. IF YOU GIVE AWAY FOUR OF THEM, YOU'LL BE ELECTED THE PRESIDENT OF THE DRAGONS' CLUB.

THE DRAGON WAS OVER-JOYED. HERE, YOU CAN KEEP THESE FOUR PEARLS. THANK YOU, CHI HUAN.

WITH THE POT FULL OF GOLD AND THE FOUR PEARLS, CHI HUAN REACHED THE INN.

KUBAYA SHI TOLD ME THAT YOUR EYESIGHT WILL COME TO YOU THE MINUTE THE HEIR TO YOUR INN TAKES A SEAT UNDER YOUR ROOF.

SO SAYING CHI HUAN SAT DOWN. SUDDENLY—

YIPPEE! I CAN SEE! HA! HA! I CAN SEE! CHI HUAN, MY EYESIGHT HAS FINALLY COME TO ME. I AM NO LONGER BLIND.

DOES THAT MEAN.....?

YES, THAT MEANS THAT YOU ARE MY HEIR. YOU MUST LOOK AFTER THE INN NOW, CHILD.

CHI HUAN WAS NOW MUCH RICHER THAN HE EVER HAD BEEN. HE WAS ALSO A LOT WISER.

I'M SURE THAT MY NAME HAS NOTHING TO DO WITH MY WEALTH. I GREW RICH BECAUSE I DECIDED TO HELP OTHERS BEFORE MYSELF.

YOU'RE RIGHT.

Dance of the Dragon

The dragon plays an important role in Chinese culture being a symbol of power, wisdom and prosperity.

On important occasions, especially during the Chinese New Year celebrations, Dragon Dances are performed by skilled teams of dancers. The dancers carry the dragon (made of cloth) on poles and raise or lower its body as it moves sinuously through the streets, chasing the 'Pearl of Wisdom' held aloft in front of the dragon by a man moving ahead of the dancers.

The dragons vary in length, from a few metres long to up to 100 metres in length.

The Dragon Dance is believed to have originated during the Han Dynasty (206 B.C. – 230 A.D.).

The Butterflies

Script: Luis Fernandes
Illustrator: Durgesh Velhal
Colourist: Umesh Sarode

ZHU WAS THE DAUGHTER OF A WEALTHY MERCHANT. SHE POSSESSED MORE TOYS THAN MOST GIRLS OF HER AGE, FEASTED ON SWEETS BROUGHT FROM DISTANT LANDS AND PLAYED ALL DAY LONG WITH HER FRIENDS. BUT SHE HAD ONE SECRET DESIRE. AND ONE DAY –

FATHER, I WANT TO STUDY. SEND ME TO SCHOOL!

SCHOOL!

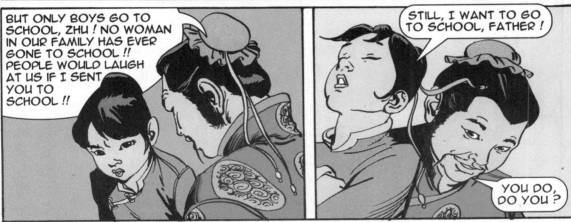

BUT ONLY BOYS GO TO SCHOOL, ZHU! NO WOMAN IN OUR FAMILY HAS EVER GONE TO SCHOOL!! PEOPLE WOULD LAUGH AT US IF I SENT YOU TO SCHOOL!!

STILL, I WANT TO GO TO SCHOOL, FATHER!

YOU DO, DO YOU?

WELL, THEN, SEE IF YOU CAN GET ADMISSION TO A SCHOOL. IF ANY SCHOOL IS WILLING TO ACCEPT YOU, I WON'T STAND IN YOUR WAY.

HER FATHER WELL KNEW THAT NO SCHOOL WOULD ADMIT A GIRL.

BUT ZHU HAD A PLAN. SHE WENT TO LIVE WITH HER AUNT IN THE CITY OF HANGZHOU...

...THERE SHE DISGUISED HERSELF AS A BOY AND SECURED ADMISSION IN A SCHOOL —

THIS WILL BE YOUR CLASSROOM...

STUDY HARD!

ZHU PROVED TO BE EXCEPTIONALLY GOOD AT HER STUDIES. ONE DAY —

YOU SHINE IN EVERY SUBJECT! WILL YOU HELP ME WITH ARITHMETIC?

WHY NOT, LIANG?

ZHU HAD NOTICED LIANG ON HER VERY FIRST DAY AT SCHOOL. SHE HAD WANTED TO TALK TO HIM BUT HAD NEVER BEEN ABLE TO MUSTER ENOUGH COURAGE TO DO SO. NOW SHE WAS THRILLED. SHE BEGAN TO COACH HIM FOR AN HOUR EVERY DAY AFTER SCHOOL.

...THEIR FRIENDSHIP GREW BY THE DAY...

...AND THEY BECAME INSEPARABLE COMPANIONS. FOUR YEARS PASSED IN THIS FASHION, THEN —

TOMORROW IS THE LAST DAY OF SCHOOL...

I KNOW!

I CANNOT BEAR THE THOUGHT OF PARTING FROM YOU, LIANG!

ME NEITHER!

I HAVE SUCH STRANGE FEELINGS FOR YOU... SOMETIMES I THINK I'M GOING MAD!

I HAVE AN IDEA... LISTEN!

NOW THAT YOUR STUDIES ARE OVER YOU WILL LOOK FOR A JOB, WON'T YOU?

YES! SO?

SEVERAL MONTHS PASSED. ZHU'S FATHER BEGAN TO MAKE PREPARATIONS FOR HER MARRIAGE, AND SHE WAS FRANTIC —

HE HAS EITHER FORGOTTEN ME OR HASN'T FOUND A GOOD JOB...

BUT HOW CAN THAT BE...

IT'S HIM!

HE HAS COME!!

?!!

HER HEART THUDDING WITH JOY AND EXCITEMENT, ZHU RAN DOWN TO THE GATE OF HER HOUSE...

...AND ONTO THE ROAD...

....AND INTO THE ARMS OF HER ASTONISHED FRIEND –

LIANG, IT'S ME, ZHU... I'M A GIRL !! I CANNOT LIVE WITHOUT YOU !!

ZHU ! MY DEAR ZHU !! IN MY HEART I KNEW IT HAD TO BE SO !!

THERE'S NO TIME TO LOSE, LIANG ! FATHER IS ARRANGING FOR MY MARRIAGE TO HIS FRIEND'S SON...

YOU MUST MEET HIM WITHOUT DELAY !

I WILL !! I HAVE A GOOD JOB, ZHU ! I'LL TAKE GOOD CARE OF YOU !!

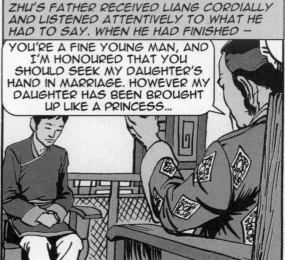

ZHU'S FATHER RECEIVED LIANG CORDIALLY AND LISTENED ATTENTIVELY TO WHAT HE HAD TO SAY. WHEN HE HAD FINISHED –

YOU'RE A FINE YOUNG MAN, AND I'M HONOURED THAT YOU SHOULD SEEK MY DAUGHTER'S HAND IN MARRIAGE. HOWEVER MY DAUGHTER HAS BEEN BROUGHT UP LIKE A PRINCESS...

SHE IS USED TO COMFORTS YOU WOULD NEVER BE ABLE TO GIVE HER. MOREOVER SHE HAS BEEN PROMISED TO ANOTHER MAN. THE MARRIAGE DATE HAS ALREADY BEEN DECIDED UPON...

BUT SIR, WE CANNOT LIVE WITHOUT EACH OTHER...PLEASE RE-CONSIDER...

LIANG DID HIS UTMOST TO CONVINCE ZHU'S FATHER TO CHANGE HIS MIND. BUT THE MERCHANT REMAINED ADAMANT. FINALLY —

ANY MORE DISCUSSION IS FUTILE. PLEASE LEAVE...

AND IF YOU TRULY LOVE HER LIKE YOU SAY, NEVER TRY TO CONTACT HER AGAIN. GIVE HER A CHANCE TO BE HAPPY WITH THE HUSBAND I'VE CHOSEN FOR HER!

LIANG STUMBLED OUT OF THE HOUSE IN A DAZE...

THEY WANT TO TAKE ZHU AWAY FROM ME...

SHE'LL MARRY SOMEONE ELSE...I'LL NEVER SEE HER AGAIN...

A VEIL OF BLACKNESS DESCENDED IN FRONT OF HIS EYES, AND THERE WAS A TIGHTNESS IN HIS CHEST. PERHAPS HE HAD A WEAK HEART, FOR SUDDENLY—

AAAAAAAA!

?!

THUMP!

MISTRESS ZHU, YOUR FRIEND...THE YOUNG MAN WHO CAME TO MEET YOUR FATHER...HE'S DEAD!

DEAD!

MISTRESS!

ZHU HOVERED BETWEEN LIFE AND DEATH FOR SEVERAL WEEKS BUT FINALLY RECOVERED. ONE DAY HER FATHER CAME IN SEARCH OF HER—

ZHU, I KNOW YOU'VE SUFFERED A GREAT LOSS...I DIDN'T KNOW HE MEANT SO MUCH TO YOU... BUT YOU CAN'T GO ON BROODING ABOUT IT...

LIFE HAS TO GO ON. A HANDSOME, YOUNG MAN IS WAITING FOR YOU TO GET OVER YOUR GRIEF AND BEGIN A NEW LIFE WITH HIM. TAKE THE OPPORTUNITY. LET US NOT POSTPONE THE MARRIAGE ANY LONGER...

ALL RIGHT, FATHER. SET THE DATE...

...BUT I HAVE ONE CONDITION... THE MARRIAGE PROCESSION MUST PASS BY THE GRAVEYARD WHERE LIANG IS BURIED....

AS YOU WISH...THAT SHOULD NOT BE A PROBLEM...

IT WAS WET AND WINDY THAT DAY. THE NOISY WEDDING PROCESSION WINDED THROUGH THE COUNTRYSIDE, TAKING A CIRCUITOUS ROUTE SO AS TO PASS BY THE CEMETERY. EVERYBODY WAS IN A FESTIVE MOOD...

...EXCEPT THE BRIDE.

69

STOP ! PUT ME DOWN !!

ZHU, WHAT ARE YOU DOING !!

ZHU, STOP !

WHAT IS THE STUPID GIRL DOING !

ZHU, STOP AT ONCE !!

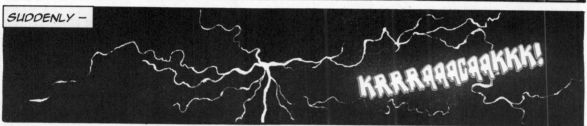